Violin Exam Pieces

ABRSM Grade 7

Selected from the syllabus from 2024

Piano accompaniment

Contents

Violin consultant: Jessica O'Leary
Footnotes: Philippa Bunting & Richard Jones (RJ)

Editorial guidance

We have taken the pieces in this book from a variety of sources. Where appropriate, we have edited the pieces to help you prepare for your performance. Editorial additions are given in small print, in square brackets or, for slurs and ties, in the form ⌢. The fingering and bowing indications have been amended where necessary to ensure a consistent approach within the album. Details of other changes or suggestions are given in the footnotes. Fingering, bowing and editorial additions are for guidance only: you do not have to follow them in the exam.

First published in 2023 by ABRSM (Publishing) Ltd, a wholly owned subsidiary of ABRSM, 4 London Wall Place, London EC2Y 5AU, United Kingdom
© 2023 by The Associated Board of the Royal Schools of Music
Distributed worldwide by Oxford University Press

Unauthorised photocopying is illegal
All rights reserved. No part of this publication may be reproduced, recorded or transmitted in any form or by any means without the prior permission of the copyright owner.

Music origination by Moira Roach
Cover by Kate Benjamin, James Pike & Andy Potts, with thanks to Sutton Music Service
Printed in England by Caligraving Ltd, Thetford, Norfolk, on materials from sustainable sources.

A:1

Allemande

Second movement from Sonata in D minor, Op. 1 No. 1

Edited by and continuo realisation
by Richard Jones

Joseph Gibbs
(1698–1788)

The English composer Joseph Gibbs was employed as an organist in the south-eastern counties of Suffolk and Essex. Around 1746 he composed eight violin sonatas in a very imaginative style. This Allemande (Gibbs uses the Italian form 'Allemanda'), selected from the sonatas, is highly intricate and expressive – rather like those of Bach and Handel. It resembles a slow movement rather than a 'German dance' – the original form and style of the Allemande. RJ

Source: *Eight Solos for a Violin with a Thorough Bass for the Harpsic[h]ord or Bass Violin* (London: Peter Thompson, n.d. [1746]). All slurs to appoggiaturas are editorial.

A:2

Allegro assai

Second movement from Sonata in B flat, Op. 6 No. 12

Edited by and continuo realisation
by Richard Jones

T. G. Albinoni
(1671–1751)

In the exam, the lower notes (D and F) in the violin chord on beat 3 of bars 6 and 44 are optional.

The Venetian musician Tomaso Giovanni Albinoni was an amateur composer – that is, he did not hold a professional post – but his works are equal in quality to those of contemporary professionals, such as Vivaldi. Ten sets of instrumental music by Albinoni were published during his lifetime. The Op. 6 sonatas, from which this piece has been selected, are described in the original edition as 'Trattenimenti armonici', which may be translated as 'Harmonic entertainments'. Dynamics are left to the player's discretion. RJ

Sources: *12 Trattenimenti armonici per camera* (Amsterdam: Etienne Roger, Le Cene; London: Walsh & Hare, n.d. [*c*.1718/20]). The music texts of the Amsterdam and London editions appear to be identical.

8

B:1

Allegretto non troppo

Op. 84

Mel Bonis
(1858–1937)

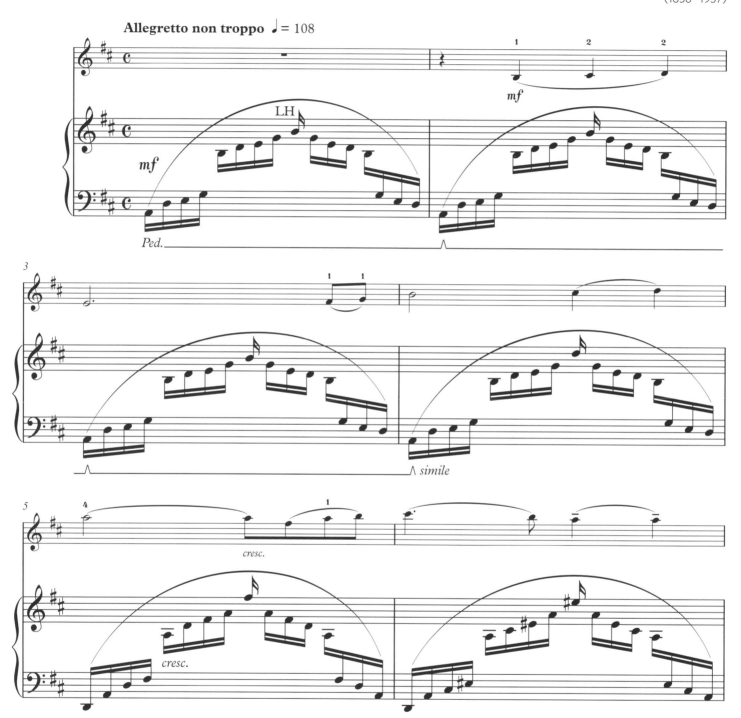

French composer Mélanie Bonis taught herself to play the piano until the age of 12 when her parents, who had been against her receiving a musical education, relented and found her a teacher. At 16 she was introduced to César Franck, who encouraged her, gave her piano lessons and later saw her admitted to the Paris Conservatoire, where she was a contemporary of Debussy. Mel Bonis was the name she adopted for her numerous published works.

In this piece, the long lines of the violin part need smooth changes at both ends of the bow, and stamina to build the phrases carefully. The harmonies in the rippling, restless piano part will influence the colours you choose for certain notes, sometimes suggesting an open, bright tone, and sometimes a more inward, muted one.

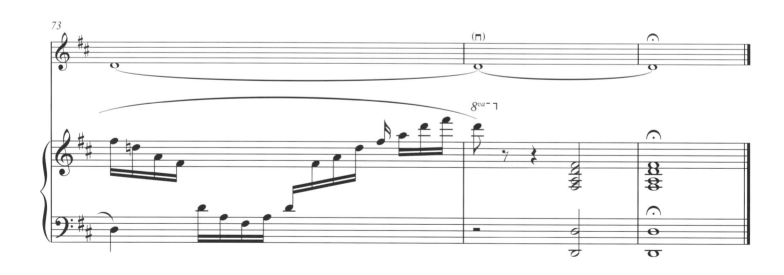

Playera

No. 1 from *Spanische Tänze*, Op. 23

Pablo de Sarasate
(1844–1908)

B:2

Spanish violinist and composer Pablo de Sarasate was commissioned to produce four sets of *Spanische Tänze* (Spanish Dances) by his publisher, who had seen the popularity that other folk-dance collections, such as Brahms's Hungarian Dances, were achieving.

The Spanish Dances were successful and Sarasate often played them as encores. Leopold Auer, a violinist contemporary, described them as 'original, inventive and effective concert pieces, so warmly coloured with the fire and romance of his native land'.

Source: *Spanische Tänze*, Op. 23 (Berlin: Simrock, n.d.[1880]). In bars 79–80, the piano has A♯ in error and this has been corrected to C♯ here. Some editorial changes have been made to the violin slurs for exam purposes.

Morceau

from Two Compositions

B:3

Ethel Barns
(1874–1948)

Ethel Barns studied violin, piano and composition at the Royal Academy of Music in London from her teenage years. She became a founding member of the Society of Women Musicians in 1911 and was a professor at the Royal Academy of Music at a time when very few women were in such a role.

Marked *affettuoso*, this is a classic salon piece, designed to illustrate the skill of the performer both to draw in the audience and to demonstrate violinistic tricks, such as the glissando down the D string in bar 21, with ease and confidence.

Source: *Two Compositions for violin and piano* (Boston: Boston Music Co., 1913). Some editorial changes have been made to the violin slurs for exam purposes.

© 2023 by The Associated Board of the Royal Schools of Music

C:1

Sérénade

No. 2 from Four Pieces, Op. 30

Anton Arensky
(1861–1906)

Mentored by Tchaikovsky, Anton Stepanovich Arensky was a Russian pianist, composer, and professor at the Moscow Conservatoire, with notable students such as Rachmaninoff and Skryabin in his class.

A serenade has its origins in music designed to attract someone's attention, then to celebrate them, and this character piece does just that. Although there are complexities in the bowing and some large shifts to navigate, the piece requires calm, effortless control throughout.

Source: *Sérénade*, Op. 30 No. 2 (Leipzig: Bosworth, 1902). The bottom note in the right-hand piano chord on the second beat of bar 38 is an E in the source, but this has been corrected to D here.

Dance of the Elves

Elfentanz

Florence B. Price
(1887–1953)

Born in Little Rock, Arkansas, Florence Price attended the New England Conservatory in Boston. However, it was after her family moved to Chicago in 1927, to escape racial violence, that her career as a composer really began to flourish.

This piece is designed to enchant, and even amuse in places. It requires a light touch, elegant bowing style, and accurate coordination between hands. The contrasting central section from bar 57 explores a Elfefent side to Price's musical style, with clear influences of spiritual melodies and gospel church music, and calls for an expansive legato sound.

C:3

Bolero

No. 3 from *Cinq morceaux caractéristiques*, Op. 51

Jenő Hubay
(1858–1937)

Hungarian musician Jenő Hubay was one of a long line of virtuoso players and composers, and a fine chamber musician. In his role as Director of the Budapest Academy of Music (1919–1934) he created one of the world's leading schools of both violin and chamber music.

This Bolero was conceived as one of five pieces celebrating the national characteristics of various countries – here, Spain. The flourishes – grace notes, arpeggio runs and harmonics – suggest an exuberant performance piece, meant for the concert platform.

Source: *Cinq morceaux caractéristiques*, Op. 51 (Leipzig: Bosworth & Co., 1894). Some editorial changes have been made to the violin slurs for exam purposes.

44

Violin Exam Pieces

ABRSM Grade 7

Selected from the 2016–2019 syllabus

Name **PELLER**

Date of exam

Contents

Violin consultant: Philippa Bunting
Footnotes: Richard Jones (RJ), David Blackwell (DB), Terence Charlston (TC) and Anthony Burton

Other pieces for Grade 7

LIST A

4 **Montanari** Adagio *and* Allegro: 1st *and* 2nd movts from Sonata No. 2 in D minor. Montanari, *The Three 'Dresden' Sonatas* (Edition HH)

5 **Rode** Air varié (*omitting var. 2*). *Sheila M. Nelson's Classical Violinist* (Boosey & Hawkes)

6 **Vivaldi** Preludio *and* Corrente: 1st *and* 2nd movts from Sonata in E minor, F. XIII No. 57, RV 17a (Ricordi)

LIST B

4 **Elgar** Mazurka. Elgar, *Ten Pieces for Violin*, Vol. 1 (Thames)

5 **Liszt** Romance oubliée, S. 132ter (PWM or Hardie Press)

6 **Moszkowski** Allegro brioso: No. 1 from *Spanische Tänze*, Op. 12, arr. Scharwenka (Peters)

LIST C

4 **Bloch** Processional: No. 2 from *Suite hébraïque* (G. Schirmer)

5 **Krzesimir Dębski** Cantabile (*observing quasi cadenza*) (PWM)

6 **Gershwin, trans. Heifetz** No. 2 from Preludes (*upper line only in octave passages*) (Alfred)

First published in 2015 by ABRSM (Publishing) Ltd, a wholly owned subsidiary of ABRSM, 24 Portland Place, London W1B 1LU, United Kingdom © 2015 by The Associated Board of the Royal Schools of Music

Music origination by Andrew Jones
Cover by Kate Benjamin & Andy Potts
Printed in England by Caligraving Ltd, Thetford, Norfolk, on materials from sustainable sources.
Reprinted in 2016.

A:1

Larghetto and Allegro
First and second movements from Sonata in A, HWV 361

Edited by and continuo
realization by Richard Jones

George Frideric Handel
(1685–1759)

Handel's Sonata in A, HWV 361, is one of three sonatas for violin and continuo that he wrote in 1724–6, while he was music master to the two princesses Anne and Caroline, daughters of the future King of England, George II. It is written in the four-movement (slow–fast–slow–fast) form of the Italian *sonata da chiesa* (church sonata). In composing sonatas of this type, Handel was clearly indebted to the tradition established by Corelli, the most celebrated instrumental composer of the age. Whereas the Larghetto is lyrical, the Allegro is fugue-like: from b. 33 the violin has to create the impression of two contrapuntal parts by means of double-stopping.

In the Larghetto, Handel's stroke above the E in b. 14 (4th crotchet) might be best treated as an accent. A similar approach might be adopted in the next bar (crotchet A) and in the Allegro, bb. 23 (3rd crotchet) and 24 (1st crotchet). RJ
Source: autograph manuscript, Cambridge, Fitzwilliam Museum, MU MS 261

4

Rondo

Third movement from Concerto in D, K. 211

Edited by and piano
reduction by David Blackwell

W. A. Mozart
(1756–91)

Candidates may play all, none or some of the tutti sections. The editorial embellishments in bb. 39, 89 and 141 are optional for the exam.

Mozart's five concertos for violin and orchestra, as well as several single movements for the same combination, were all written in 1773 and 1775, when the composer served as leader of the court musicians in Salzburg. As a competent violinist, Mozart is likely to have performed the concertos himself, but he also had a number of outstanding players available, such as the court's soloist Antonio Brunetti. Mozart's starting-point for his violin concertos was the three-movement form popularized by Vivaldi, including the alternation of tutti and solo sections, but he expanded this considerably in the five works, developing form, technique and content with increasing sophistication and maturity. The fermatas in bb. 39, 89 and 141 signal to the performer that an Eingang, or 'lead in', may be played before the return of the rondo theme.

In b. 30, the third left-hand note is written A in the source; this appears to be wrong and has been replaced by a written F♯. In b. 140 the violin notes in the source are slurred in pairs. DB
Source: autograph score, Biblioteka Jagiellońska, Kraków

Allegro

Second movement from Sonata in E, BWV 1016

Edited by Terence Charlston

J. S. Bach
(1685–1750)

Bach's early biographer, Forkel, suggests that his set of six sonatas for violin and obbligato harpsichord were written in Cöthen (1717–23). However, they were revised into their present form during his tenure as cantor and music director at St Thomas, Leipzig, from 1723 onwards. This edition is made from the earliest surviving manuscript of the final version of the set. The sonatas are not 'duo' sonatas in the Classical sense, but are rather Baroque trio sonatas with the right hand of the keyboard functioning as a 'second violin' and the left hand taking the basso continuo line. All three parts are equally important.

    While the dynamics in Bach's music are generally left to the player's discretion, the *piano* in the violin part in b. 79 is original, and all other dynamics are editorial. Such 'courtesy' dynamics are indicative of the relative importance of musical ideas (f = solo, p = accompaniment) and should be adjusted in performance (e.g. at b. 63) to achieve an appropriate balance. Slurs that are ambiguously drawn in the source have been unified in parallel passages in this edition. Two pitch errors have been corrected: b. 23, violin, note 4 is given as e"; and b. 122, right hand of keyboard, note 8 is given as d"♮. The ornaments in the keyboard part in bb. 23 and 79 are suggestions from a later manuscript by Bach's second surviving son, Carl Philipp Emanuel Bach. In the source at b. 34 the dotted crotchet is given as a crotchet tied to a quaver; this has been adjusted by analogy with b. 33. TC

Source: Manuscript in the hand of Bach's pupil, Johann Christoph Altnickol, Berlin, Staatsbibliothek zu Berlin – Preussischer Kulturbesitz, Musikabteilung, Mus.ms.Bach P 229

12

Introduction and Polonaise

No. 12 from *Arabesken*

B:1

Edited by Richard Jones

Carl Bohm
(1844–1920)

Introduction

Molto moderato ed espressivo [♩ = c.72]

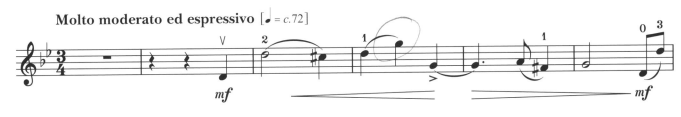

The German composer and pianist Carl Bohm specialized in music written in a lighter vein. His many chamber works, piano pieces and songs proved so popular that his publisher Simrock reportedly claimed that the profits on the sale of his music financed the publication of the works of Brahms. Bohm's *Arabesken* consists of 12 pieces for violin and piano, published in two instalments in 1894 and 1895. Arabesques – ornaments often found in Arabic art and architecture (and elsewhere) – were frequently imitated in decorative musical compositions of the 19th century, notably those of Schumann.

The polonaise was originally a festive couple dance of Polish origin, in a moderate tempo. By the 18th century it had become a stylized instrumental dance, and during the 19th century it spread throughout Europe and was cultivated, above all, by Chopin. It is characterized by the absence of upbeats and by certain repeated rhythmic figures (see, for example, the piano part in bb. 35–6). In b. 68, the violin is marked *cresc.* in the source; this appears to be wrong and the cresc. is given in this edition in b. 69. RJ

Source: *Arabesken. 12 Vorspielstücke für Violine mit Begleitung des Pianoforte*, Vol. 2 (Berlin: Simrock, 1895)

Polonaise

B:2

Allegro

No. 4 from *Southland Sketches*

H. T. Burleigh
(1866–1949)

Henry (Harry) Burleigh occupies an honoured place in musical history as the African American student at the National Conservatory of Music in New York who sang spirituals to the Conservatory's director Antonín Dvořák, providing the inspiration for some of the themes of Dvořák's 'New World' Symphony. Burleigh went on to enjoy a long and successful career as a solo singer in St George's Episcopal Church, New York, and in concerts. He also made many arrangements of spirituals, and composed numerous songs and a handful of instrumental pieces. The four *Southland Sketches*, inspired by the African American music of the southern United States, were published in New York in 1916.

Source: *Southland Sketches* (New York: G. Ricordi & Co., 1916)

Souvenir

František Drdla
(1869–1944)

Use of the mute is optional in the exam.

The violinist and composer František, or Franz, Drdla was born in Moravia, now part of the Czech Republic. After studying in Prague and Vienna, he became the leader of the orchestra of the historic Theater an der Wien in Vienna. He later made concert tours of Europe and the USA as a soloist. His compositions include two operettas and a violin concerto; but he is best remembered for his shorter salon pieces for violin, which often feature portamento slides between notes, as here. *Souvenir* was published in 1904 and was recorded by several celebrated violinists of the early 20th century, including Fritz Kreisler, Jan Kubelík and Maud Powell.

© Josef Weinberger Limited

This edition reprinted by permission of the copyright owner. All enquiries about this piece, apart from those directly relating to the exams, should be addressed to Josef Weinberger Limited, 12–14 Mortimer Street, London W1T 3JJ.

Prelude and Waltz

No. 1 and No. 3 from Five Pieces, Op. 84

Malcolm Arnold
(1921–2006)

I Prelude

Con energico ♩ = 100

sempre non staccato e molto rubato

Sir Malcolm Arnold was one of the most successful and prolific British composers of his time, responsible for over 100 film scores and numerous concert works. He wrote the Five Pieces for the celebrated violinist Yehudi Menuhin to play as encores on a tour of America in 1964. The first is a Prelude with lean contrapuntal textures reminiscent of the music of Paul Hindemith; the third is a delicate Waltz, full of turns of harmony and melody characteristic of the composer. Although the original metronome mark for the Prelude is ♩ = 100, a slightly slower tempo of ♩ = *c*.92 would be acceptable in the exam.

III Waltz

Grazioso ♩ = 100

Rojo y negro

C:2

Ramiro Gallo
born 1966

Rojo y negro Red and Black

Ramiro Gallo is an Argentine violinist who leads or plays in several tango groups, and a composer who has written extensively for those groups. He is also the author of a tutor called *El violín en el tango* ('The Violin in Tango'), from which this piece is selected. The red and black of the title refer to a combination of colours traditionally associated with the tango, and also with the composer's favourite football team Club Atlético Colón de Santa Fe. The piece is in the genre of the *milonga ciudadana* ('city milonga'): the milonga was a forerunner of the tango, but this faster variety emerged in the 1930s and has held a place in the repertoire. The *látigo* ('whip') effect in bar 7 is a familiar feature of tango violin playing, a fast glissando to an extreme high note.

© 2010 by EPSA Publishing SA, Buenos Aires, Argentina
International copyright secured. All enquiries about this piece, apart from those directly relating to the exams, should be addressed to EPSA Publishing SA at info@epsapublishing.com.

24

C:3

Gavotte with Two Variations

No. 4 from *Suite italienne*

Arranged by Igor Stravinsky
and Samuel Dushkin

Igor Stravinsky
(1882–1971)

Igor Stravinsky's 'Italian Suite' is an arrangement, made in 1932 in collaboration with the Russian American violinist Samuel Dushkin, of movements from Stravinsky's 1920 ballet score *Pulcinella*. At the suggestion of Sergey Diaghilev, the impresario of the Ballets Russes company, the ballet was based on music by, or attributed to, the short-lived 18th-century Italian composer Giovanni Battista Pergolesi. In fact, the 'Gavotte with Two Variations' is now known to be a reworking of a piece for harpsichord by the Milan composer Carlo Ignazio Monza (d. 1739). Stravinsky treated the piece very freely in what was to become known as his 'neoclassical' manner, adding new harmonies and countermelodies which suggest a kind of creative collaboration across the centuries.

Variation 2

Allegretto più tosto moderato [♩ = c.80]